Franklin

GOES TO DAY CAMP

A Story and
Activity Book

ISBN 0-439-40769-9

12 11 10 9 8 7 6 5 4 3 2 1   2 3 4 5 6 7/0

Printed in the U.S.A.   23

First Scholastic Book Club printing, April 2002

Franklin
GOES TO DAY CAMP

A Story and Activity Book

Paulette Bourgeois • Brenda Clark
Activities by Jane B. Mason

SCHOLASTIC INC.
New York   Toronto   London   Auckland   Sydney
Mexico City   New Delhi   Hong Kong   Buenos Aires

FRANKLIN could swim the length of the pond and row a boat. He knew the words to two campfire songs, and he'd even had a sleepover at Bear's house. But Franklin was worried. He was going to day camp for the very first time, and he didn't know if he would like it.

At breakfast Franklin asked his mother, "What will I do at camp?"

"Lots of fun things, I imagine," she answered.

Franklin packed his camp bag. He needed a hat and sunscreen, a towel and raingear.

"You'll need your colored pencils, too," said Franklin's mother.

"Camp isn't like school, is it?" asked Franklin.

His mother laughed. "Camp is even better than school," she said.

Franklin's tummy did flip-flops when the camp bus pulled up in front of his house.

"Have fun and play safe," said his parents.

Franklin got on. All his friends were there.

The camp counselor was on the bus, too. She gave every camper a little book.

"This is your journal," she told them. "Each day you fill it in. By the end of the week, you'll have pages of memories."

"I hope they're good ones," grumbled Beaver.

The bus bumped along the road, and soon they were at camp.

"I wonder what we'll do first," said Franklin.

FRANKLIN'S Day Camp *Journal*

Day 1
Today we took a walk in the woods. Then we had a picnic at the duck pond.

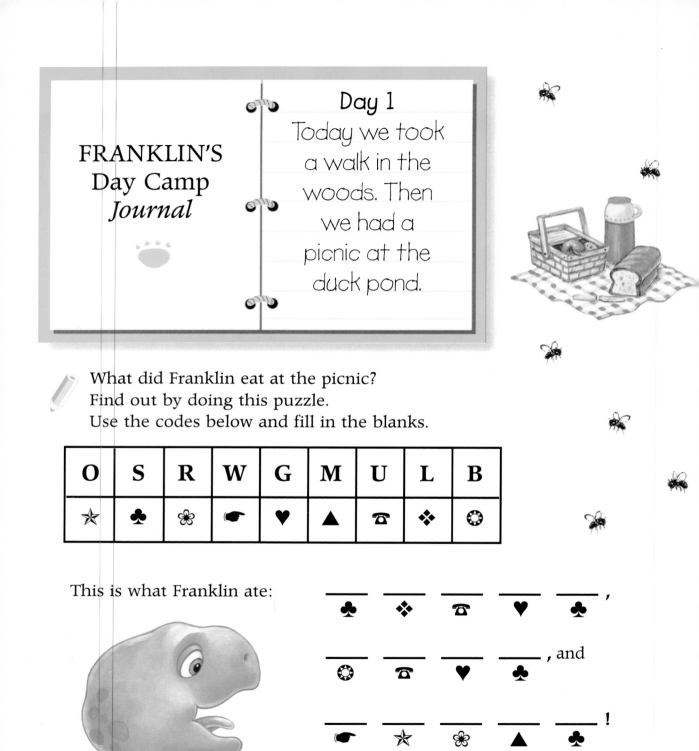

What did Franklin eat at the picnic?
Find out by doing this puzzle.
Use the codes below and fill in the blanks.

O	S	R	W	G	M	U	L	B
☆	♣	✿	☞	♥	▲	☎	❖	◉

This is what Franklin ate:

_♣_ _❖_ _☎_ _♥_ _♣_ ,

_◉_ _☎_ _♥_ _♣_ , and

_☞_ _☆_ _✿_ _▲_ _♣_ !

Turn to page 24 to check your answers to all the puzzles in this book.

Can you find the path the campers took to get to the duck pond?

START

FINISH

9

FRANKLIN'S Day Camp *Journal*

Day 2
Today was Hat Day. We each wore a special hat to camp. It was fun to wear it all day long!

Franklin has a lot of different hats.
Which one did he choose for Hat Day?
To find the answer, cross out the letters
N, B, and **Z** below. Then write the other
letters in the blanks.

N B H Z N I S B S A N I L Z O B R N C N A Z P

__ __ __   __ __ __ __ __ __   __ __ __

is the hat that Franklin wore on Hat Day.

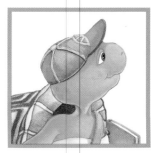

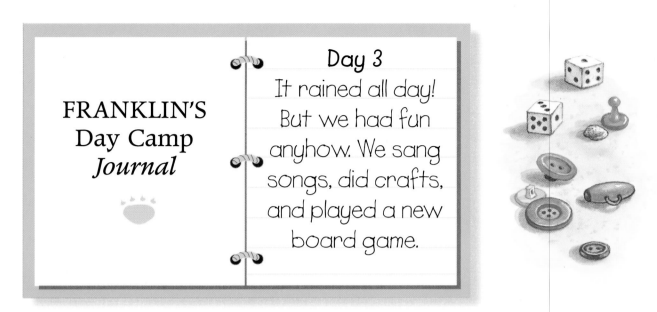

**FRANKLIN'S
Day Camp
*Journal***

Day 3
It rained all day!
But we had fun
anyhow. We sang
songs, did crafts,
and played a new
board game.

Hop, Skip, and Jump! Board Game

The game on the next two pages is an obstacle course you have to get through as fast as you can. The first player to land on FINISH wins.

Here is what you need to play:
- a playing piece for each person (you can use different-colored buttons or other small objects)
- a die
- the game board on the next two pages

Here is how to play:
1. Each person puts a playing piece at START.
2. Take turns rolling the die and moving.
3. If you land on a special space, follow the directions.
4. It's okay to have more than one person on a square.
5. The first person to land on FINISH wins. If you don't roll the exact number you need, wait until your next turn to try again.

Hop, Skip, and Jump!

START

You find the right path. Skip ahead 3 spaces.

You are chased by a bumblebee. Hop back 2 spaces.

You trip on a rock. Hop back 1 space.

You cross the stream. Jump ahead 2 spaces.

You zigzag around some tree stumps. Skip ahead 3 spaces.

You find
a shortcut.
Skip ahead
2 spaces.

You fall out
of a tree.
Hop back
1 space.

You slip on
wet grass.
Hop back
2 spaces.

You leap over
a mud puddle.
Jump ahead
3 spaces.

You get stuck
in a hollow log.
Hop back
1 space.

FINISH!

**FRANKLIN'S
Day Camp
*Journal***

Day 4
It was Sports Day.
My team won a
ribbon in the race.

Franklin and six of his friends are in a race.
Unscramble the letters to spell all their names.

N A F K L R I N   — — — — — — —

O G S O E   — — — — —

V E B E A R   — — — — — —

E B A R   — — — —

A B R I B T   — — — — — —

K D U C   — — — —

O X F   — — —

15

FRANKLIN'S Day Camp *Journal*

Campfire Night

We had a special campfire night. Bear and I cooked hot dogs over the fire. Yum!

Here is a campfire crossword puzzle for you to do.
Read the clues and fill in the spaces in the puzzle.

Across

3. On Campfire Night, Bear and Franklin cook these over the fire.

5. Bear and Franklin are best _____.

6. After the campfire, the counselor reads the campers a _____.

7. It's dark out at _____.

9. This is how the hot dogs taste to Franklin and Bear.

Down

1. You need this to make a campfire.

2. The hot dogs are_____ over the fire.

4. These shine in the sky at night.

8. Franklin has one hot dog, but Bear has _____.

Words to use in this puzzle:
friends
roasting
wood
good
stars
hot dogs
story
night
two

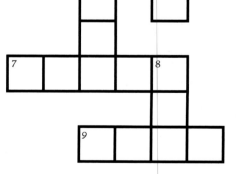

FRANKLIN'S Day Camp *Journal*

Day 5
The last day of camp! We played sports and had all kinds of fun.

On Sports Day, the campers enjoyed many different sports. Can you find the eight sports words in the word search puzzle? (Hint: The words go across and down.) The first one is done for you.

~~KICK~~   SOCCER   DIVE

GOAL   COACH   BASEBALL

STRIKE   SWIM   BAT

C B A T B C S

K I C K A O T

S O M R S A R

O D I V E C I

C S L G B H K

C W G O A L E

E I H A L J Z

R M O S L Q R

19

By the end of the week, Franklin had played on the swings and learned a new board game. He had passed a swimming test and hit a home run. He had made a bowl from clay and a whistle from a blade of grass. And he had even learned four new songs with actions.

"Did you enjoy your week at camp?" Franklin's
mother asked.

"It was great!" said Franklin. "See?"

He flipped through the pages in his journal.
"That's only part of what we did!" he said. "There's
just one problem."

Franklin's parents looked worried.

"What is it?" his father asked.

"It's all over!" moaned Franklin.
Then he had a happy thought.
"Maybe next year," he said, "I can go for two weeks and have twice as much fun!"

FRANKLIN'S Day Camp *Journal*

My Day Camp Favorites
1. Seeing friends
2. Swimming
3. Playing games
4. Catching flies

Franklin made a list of his favorite things about day camp. Write down your favorite things about day camp. (If you don't go to day camp, write down your favorite things about summer.)

1. _____

2. _____

3. _____

4. _____

Answer Page

Page 8

SLUGS, BUGS, and WORMS!

Page 9

Page 10

N̶B̶H̶Z̶N̶IS̶B̶SA̶N̶IL̶Z̶O̶B̶R̶N̶C̶N̶A̶Z̶P̶

HIS SAILOR CAP

Page 15

FRANKLIN
GOOSE
BEAVER
BEAR
RABBIT
DUCK
FOX

Page 17

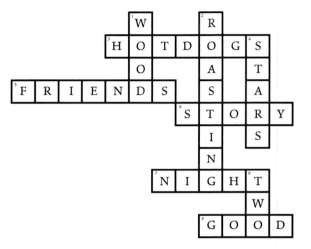

Page 19

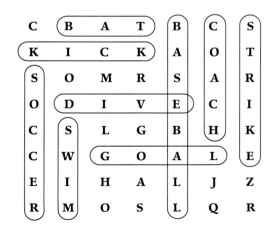